# Happy Journal

## How To Find Your Happy

GW00776875

Happiness Planner & Journal in One

*This Journal Belongs To*

_____

Day _____ Date _____

Today I Am Happy Because:

_____

_____

_____

_____

_____

_____

"Do not spoil what you have by desiring what you
have not; remember that what you now
have was once among the things
you only hoped for." — Epicurus

Daily Journal

_____

_____

_____

_____

_____

_____

_____

_____

Day _____  Date _____

Today I Am Happy Because:

---------------------------------------------------

---------------------------------------------------

---------------------------------------------------

---------------------------------------------------

---------------------------------------------------

---------------------------------------------------

"Let gratitude be the pillow upon which you kneel to say
your nightly prayer. And let faith be the bridge you
build to overcome evil and welcome good."
— Maya Angelou

Daily Journal

---------------------------------------------------

---------------------------------------------------

---------------------------------------------------

---------------------------------------------------

---------------------------------------------------

---------------------------------------------------

---------------------------------------------------

---------------------------------------------------

Day _____  Date _____

Today I Am Happy Because:

_____

_____

_____

_____

_____

_____

"Acknowledging the good that you already have in
your life is the foundation for all abundance."
— Eckhart Tolle

Daily Journal

_____

_____

_____

_____

_____

_____

_____

_____

Day _____ Date _____

Today I Am Happy Because:

----------------------------------------------------------------

----------------------------------------------------------------

----------------------------------------------------------------

----------------------------------------------------------------

----------------------------------------------------------------

----------------------------------------------------------------

"Forget yesterday - it has already forgotten you.
Don't sweat tomorrow - you haven't even met.
Instead, open your eyes and your heart to a truly
precious gift - today."
— Steve Maraboli

Daily Journal

----------------------------------------------------------------

----------------------------------------------------------------

----------------------------------------------------------------

----------------------------------------------------------------

----------------------------------------------------------------

----------------------------------------------------------------

----------------------------------------------------------------

----------------------------------------------------------------

Day _____ Date _____

Today I Am Happy Because:

_____

_____

_____

_____

_____

_____

*"Some people grumble that roses have thorns; I am
grateful that thorns have roses."*
*— Alphonse Karr*

## Daily Journal

_____

_____

_____

_____

_____

_____

_____

_____

Day _____ Date _____

Today I Am Happy Because:

_____

_____

_____

_____

_____

_____

*"Gratitude is not only the greatest of virtues, but the parent of all others."*
*— Marcus Tullius Cicero*

## Daily Journal

_____

_____

_____

_____

_____

_____

_____

_____

Day _____ Date _____

Today I Am Happy Because:

_____

_____

_____

_____

_____

_____

"God gave you a gift of 86 400 seconds today. Have
you used one to say thank you"
— William Arthur Ward

Daily Journal

_____

_____

_____

_____

_____

_____

_____

_____

Day _____  Date _____

Today I Am Happy Because:

_____

_____

_____

_____

_____

_____

*"Gratitude looks to the Past and love to the Present; fear, avarice, lust, and ambition look ahead."*
*— C.S. Lewis*

## Daily Journal

_____

_____

_____

_____

_____

_____

_____

_____

Day _____ Date _____

Today I Am Happy Because:

_____

_____

_____

_____

_____

_____

"I would maintain that thanks are the highest form
of thought; and that gratitude is happiness doubled
by wonder". ~G.K. Chesterton

<u>Daily Journal</u>

_____

_____

_____

_____

_____

_____

_____

_____

Day _____ Date _____

Today I Am Happy Because:

-----------------------------------------------------------

-----------------------------------------------------------

-----------------------------------------------------------

-----------------------------------------------------------

-----------------------------------------------------------

-----------------------------------------------------------

*"When you are grateful, fear disappears and abundance appears."*
*— Anthony Robbins*

## Daily Journal

-----------------------------------------------------------

-----------------------------------------------------------

-----------------------------------------------------------

-----------------------------------------------------------

-----------------------------------------------------------

-----------------------------------------------------------

-----------------------------------------------------------

Day _____  Date _____

Today I Am Happy Because:

------------------------------------------------

------------------------------------------------

------------------------------------------------

------------------------------------------------

------------------------------------------------

------------------------------------------------

*"Feeling gratitude and not expressing it is like
wrapping a present and not giving it."*
*— William Arthur Ward*

## Daily Journal

------------------------------------------------

------------------------------------------------

------------------------------------------------

------------------------------------------------

------------------------------------------------

------------------------------------------------

------------------------------------------------

------------------------------------------------

Day _____  Date _____

Today I Am Happy Because:

-----------------------------------------------------------

-----------------------------------------------------------

-----------------------------------------------------------

-----------------------------------------------------------

-----------------------------------------------------------

-----------------------------------------------------------

"The world is 3 days: As for yesterday, it has vanished
along with all that was in it. As for tomorrow, you
may never see it. As for today, it is yours, so work on
it." — al-Hasan al-Basri

Daily Journal

-----------------------------------------------------------

-----------------------------------------------------------

-----------------------------------------------------------

-----------------------------------------------------------

-----------------------------------------------------------

-----------------------------------------------------------

-----------------------------------------------------------

-----------------------------------------------------------

-----------------------------------------------------------

Day _____ Date _____

Today I Am Happy Because:

_____

_____

_____

_____

_____

_____

"After every storm, there is a rainbow. If you have
eyes, you will find it. If you have wisdom, you will
create it. If you have love for yourself and others, you
won't need it." — Shannon L. Alder

## Daily Journal

_____

_____

_____

_____

_____

_____

_____

_____

Day _____ Date _____

Today I Am Happy Because:

------------------------------------------------

------------------------------------------------

------------------------------------------------

------------------------------------------------

------------------------------------------------

------------------------------------------------

"Regardless of Sunshine or Rain, Be Thankful for
another GREAT day…and treat Life as the
ULTIMATE Gift…. Because IT IS :)"
— Pablo

Daily Journal

------------------------------------------------

------------------------------------------------

------------------------------------------------

------------------------------------------------

------------------------------------------------

------------------------------------------------

------------------------------------------------

------------------------------------------------

Day _____  Date _____

Today I Am Happy Because:

---------------------------------------------------

---------------------------------------------------

---------------------------------------------------

---------------------------------------------------

---------------------------------------------------

---------------------------------------------------

"The unthankful heart discovers no mercies; but the
thankful heart will find, in every hour, some
heavenly blessings." — Henry Ward Beecher

## Daily Journal

---------------------------------------------------

---------------------------------------------------

---------------------------------------------------

---------------------------------------------------

---------------------------------------------------

---------------------------------------------------

---------------------------------------------------

---------------------------------------------------

Day _____    Date _____

Today I Am Happy Because:

----------------------------------------------------------

----------------------------------------------------------

----------------------------------------------------------

----------------------------------------------------------

----------------------------------------------------------

----------------------------------------------------------

"For each new morning with its light,
For rest and shelter of the night,
For health and food, for love and friends,
For everything Thy goodness sends."
— Ralph Waldo Emerson

Daily Journal

----------------------------------------------------------

----------------------------------------------------------

----------------------------------------------------------

----------------------------------------------------------

----------------------------------------------------------

----------------------------------------------------------

----------------------------------------------------------

----------------------------------------------------------

Day _____ Date _____

Today I Am Happy Because:

_____

_____

_____

_____

_____

_____

*"When it comes to life the critical thing is whether
you take things for granted or take them
with gratitude."*
— *G.K. Chesterton*

## Daily Journal

_____

_____

_____

_____

_____

_____

_____

_____

Day _____  Date _____

Today I Am Happy Because:

_____

_____

_____

_____

_____

_____

*"Take full account of what Excellences you possess,*
*and in gratitude remember how you would hanker*
*after them, if you had them not."*
*— Marcus Aurelius*

<u>Daily Journal</u>

_____

_____

_____

_____

_____

_____

_____

_____

Day _____ Date _____

Today I Am Happy Because:

_____

_____

_____

_____

_____

_____


"I may not be where I want to be but I'm thankful for
not being where I used to be."
— Habeeb Akande


## Daily Journal

_____

_____

_____

_____

_____

_____

_____

_____

Day _____ Date _____

Today I Am Happy Because:

-----------------------------------------------------------

-----------------------------------------------------------

-----------------------------------------------------------

-----------------------------------------------------------

-----------------------------------------------------------

-----------------------------------------------------------

*"The miracle is not to walk on water. The miracle is
to walk on the green earth, dwelling deeply in the
present moment and feeling truly alive."*
*— Thích Nhất Hạnh*

## Daily Journal

-----------------------------------------------------------

-----------------------------------------------------------

-----------------------------------------------------------

-----------------------------------------------------------

-----------------------------------------------------------

-----------------------------------------------------------

-----------------------------------------------------------

-----------------------------------------------------------

Day _____ Date _____

Today I Am Happy Because:

_____

_____

_____

_____

_____

_____

*"Be happy, noble heart, be blessed for all the good
thou hast done and wilt do hereafter, and let my
gratitude remain in obscurity like your good deeds."
— Alexandre Dumas*

## Daily Journal

_____

_____

_____

_____

_____

_____

_____

_____

Day _____ Date _____

Today I Am Happy Because:

----------------------------------------------------------

----------------------------------------------------------

----------------------------------------------------------

----------------------------------------------------------

----------------------------------------------------------

----------------------------------------------------------

"Courtesies of a small and trivial character are the
ones which strike deepest in the grateful and
appreciating heart."
— Henry Clay

Daily Journal

----------------------------------------------------------

----------------------------------------------------------

----------------------------------------------------------

----------------------------------------------------------

----------------------------------------------------------

----------------------------------------------------------

----------------------------------------------------------

----------------------------------------------------------

Day _____ Date _____

Today I Am Happy Because:

_____

_____

_____

_____

_____

_____

"A little "thank you" that you will say to someone for
a "little favour" shown to you is a key to unlock the
doors that hide unseen "greater favours". Learn to
say "thank you" and why not?"
— Israelmore Ayivor

Daily Journal

_____

_____

_____

_____

_____

_____

_____

_____

Day _____ Date _____

Today I Am Happy Because:

-------------------------------------------------------

-------------------------------------------------------

-------------------------------------------------------

-------------------------------------------------------

-------------------------------------------------------

-------------------------------------------------------

"Gratitude always comes into play; research shows
that people are happier if they are grateful for the
positive things in their lives, rather than worrying
about what might be missing."
— Dan Buettner

## Daily Journal

-------------------------------------------------------

-------------------------------------------------------

-------------------------------------------------------

-------------------------------------------------------

-------------------------------------------------------

-------------------------------------------------------

-------------------------------------------------------

-------------------------------------------------------

Day _____ Date _____

Today I Am Happy Because:

_____

_____

_____

_____

_____

_____

"Summoning gratitude is a sure way to get our life
back on track. Opening our eyes to affirm gratitude
grows the garden of our inner abundance, just as
standing close to a fire eventually warms our heart."
— Alexandra Katehakis

Daily Journal

_____

_____

_____

_____

_____

_____

_____

_____

Day _____  Date _____

Today I Am Happy Because:

---------------------------------------------------

---------------------------------------------------

---------------------------------------------------

---------------------------------------------------

---------------------------------------------------

---------------------------------------------------

"When you express gratitude for the blessings that
come into your life, it not only encourages the
universe to send you more, it also sees to it
that those blessings remain."
— Stephen Richards

Daily Journal

---------------------------------------------------

---------------------------------------------------

---------------------------------------------------

---------------------------------------------------

---------------------------------------------------

---------------------------------------------------

---------------------------------------------------

---------------------------------------------------

Day _____ Date _____

Today I Am Happy Because:

---------------------------------------------------------------

---------------------------------------------------------------

---------------------------------------------------------------

---------------------------------------------------------------

---------------------------------------------------------------

---------------------------------------------------------------

"Gratitude and love are always multiplied when you
give freely. It is an infinite source of contentment
and prosperous energy."
— Jim Fargiano

## Daily Journal

---------------------------------------------------------------

---------------------------------------------------------------

---------------------------------------------------------------

---------------------------------------------------------------

---------------------------------------------------------------

---------------------------------------------------------------

---------------------------------------------------------------

Day _____ Date _____

Today I Am Happy Because:

------------------------------------------------

------------------------------------------------

------------------------------------------------

------------------------------------------------

------------------------------------------------

------------------------------------------------

*"Don't count your blessings, let your blessings count!*
*Enjoy Life!"*
*— Bernard Kelvin Clive*

## Daily Journal

------------------------------------------------

------------------------------------------------

------------------------------------------------

------------------------------------------------

------------------------------------------------

------------------------------------------------

------------------------------------------------

------------------------------------------------

Day _____  Date _____

Today I Am Happy Because:

------------------------------------------------

------------------------------------------------

------------------------------------------------

------------------------------------------------

------------------------------------------------

------------------------------------------------

"Most of us forget to take time for wonder, praise and
gratitude until it is almost too late. Gratitude is a
many-colored quality, reaching in all directions. It
goes out for small things and for large; it is a God-
ward going." — Faith Baldwin

<u>Daily Journal</u>

------------------------------------------------

------------------------------------------------

------------------------------------------------

------------------------------------------------

------------------------------------------------

------------------------------------------------

------------------------------------------------

------------------------------------------------

Day _____ Date _____

Today I Am Happy Because:

_____

_____

_____

_____

_____

_____

"No one can obtain felicity by pursuit. This explains
why one of the elements of being happy is the feeling
that a debt of gratitude is owed, a debt impossible to
pay. Now, we do not owe gratitude to ourselves. To be
conscious of gratitude is to acknowledge a gift."
— Josef Pieper

Daily Journal

_____

_____

_____

_____

_____

_____

_____

_____

Day _____ Date _____

Today I Am Happy Because:

------------------------------------------------

------------------------------------------------

------------------------------------------------

------------------------------------------------

------------------------------------------------

------------------------------------------------

*"When I think of how many people in this world have it worse than I do, I realize just how blessed I really am...... and I have to give thanks ..."*
*— Shannan Lea*

## Daily Journal

------------------------------------------------

------------------------------------------------

------------------------------------------------

------------------------------------------------

------------------------------------------------

------------------------------------------------

------------------------------------------------

------------------------------------------------

Day _____ Date _____

Today I Am Happy Because:

_____

_____

_____

_____

_____

_____

"I try hard to hold fast to the truth that a full and
thankful heart cannot entertain great conceits.
When brimming with gratitude, one's heartbeat
must surely result in outgoing love, the finest
emotion we can ever know."
— Bill W

Daily Journal

_____

_____

_____

_____

_____

_____

_____

_____

_____

Day _____ Date _____

Today I Am Happy Because:

_____

_____

_____

_____

_____

_____

*"Though they only take a second to say, thank yous leave a warm feeling behind that can last for hours."*
*— Kent Allan Rees*

## Daily Journal

_____

_____

_____

_____

_____

_____

_____

_____

Day _____   Date _____

Today I Am Happy Because:

---------------------------------------------

---------------------------------------------

---------------------------------------------

---------------------------------------------

---------------------------------------------

---------------------------------------------

*"Lord I thank you for the gift of breath, eyes to see, ears to hear, tongue to taste, nose to smell, mouth to speak, face to smile, voice to sing, body to dance, legs to walk, mind to think and hands to write."*
— Lailah Gifty Akita

## Daily Journal

---------------------------------------------

---------------------------------------------

---------------------------------------------

---------------------------------------------

---------------------------------------------

---------------------------------------------

---------------------------------------------

Day _____ Date _____

Today I Am Happy Because:

_____

_____

_____

_____

_____

_____

*"Gratitude is the antidote for misery. When you are counting your blessings you are too busy to be counting your problems."*
*— Miya Yamanouchi*

## Daily Journal

_____

_____

_____

_____

_____

_____

_____

_____

Day _____ Date _____

Today I Am Happy Because:

----------------------------------------

----------------------------------------

----------------------------------------

----------------------------------------

----------------------------------------

----------------------------------------

*"The greatest of blessings can come from what appear to be the smallest and most insignificant of things. Don't discredit anything or anyone. One person, one tiny thing, one little shift can change your life in enormous ways." — Patience W. Smith*

## Daily Journal

----------------------------------------

----------------------------------------

----------------------------------------

----------------------------------------

----------------------------------------

----------------------------------------

----------------------------------------

----------------------------------------

Day _____ Date _____

Today I Am Happy Because:

-------------------------------------------------

-------------------------------------------------

-------------------------------------------------

-------------------------------------------------

-------------------------------------------------

-------------------------------------------------

*"Gratitude is a divine shift in your perspective from one of separation and lack to one of unity and right mindedness. It is a choice not made from guilt but rather from a higher level of consciousness."*
*— Janet Rebhan*

Daily Journal

-------------------------------------------------

-------------------------------------------------

-------------------------------------------------

-------------------------------------------------

-------------------------------------------------

-------------------------------------------------

-------------------------------------------------

-------------------------------------------------

Day _____  Date _____

Today I Am Happy Because:

---------------------------------------------------------------

---------------------------------------------------------------

---------------------------------------------------------------

---------------------------------------------------------------

---------------------------------------------------------------

---------------------------------------------------------------

*"Gratitude is a divine emotion. It fills the heart, not to bursting; it warms it, but not to fever. I like to taste leisurely of bliss. Devoured in haste, I do not know its flavor."— Charlotte Brontë*

Daily Journal

---------------------------------------------------------------

---------------------------------------------------------------

---------------------------------------------------------------

---------------------------------------------------------------

---------------------------------------------------------------

---------------------------------------------------------------

---------------------------------------------------------------

---------------------------------------------------------------

Day _____ Date _____

Today I Am Happy Because:

_____

_____

_____

_____

_____

_____

"Road accidents, psycho killings, plane crashes
abound - we don't know which day will be our last,
so why not make today the happiest day and be
thankful for all that we have?"
— Maddy Malhotra

Daily Journal

_____

_____

_____

_____

_____

_____

_____

_____

Day _____  Date _____

Today I Am Happy Because:

------------------------------------------------

------------------------------------------------

------------------------------------------------

------------------------------------------------

------------------------------------------------

------------------------------------------------

*"Gratitude for all the beauty and blessings that we already enjoy fills our lives with abundance."*
*— Debasish Mridha*

<u>Daily Journal</u>

------------------------------------------------

------------------------------------------------

------------------------------------------------

------------------------------------------------

------------------------------------------------

------------------------------------------------

------------------------------------------------

------------------------------------------------

Day _____ Date _____

Today I Am Happy Because:

------------------------------------------------------

------------------------------------------------------

------------------------------------------------------

------------------------------------------------------

------------------------------------------------------

------------------------------------------------------

*"Be grateful for what you already have while you pursue what you want."*
*— Roy Bennett*

<u>Daily Journal</u>

------------------------------------------------------

------------------------------------------------------

------------------------------------------------------

------------------------------------------------------

------------------------------------------------------

------------------------------------------------------

------------------------------------------------------

------------------------------------------------------

Day _____ Date _____

Today I Am Happy Because:

------------------------------------------------------

------------------------------------------------------

------------------------------------------------------

------------------------------------------------------

------------------------------------------------------

------------------------------------------------------

*"By talking to yourself every hour of the day, you can direct yourself to think thoughts of courage and happiness, thoughts of power and peace. By talking to yourself about the things you have to be grateful for, you can fill your mind with thoughts that soar and sing." — Dale Carnegie*

## Daily Journal

------------------------------------------------------

------------------------------------------------------

------------------------------------------------------

------------------------------------------------------

------------------------------------------------------

------------------------------------------------------

------------------------------------------------------

------------------------------------------------------

Day _____ Date _____

Today I Am Happy Because:

----------------------------------------

----------------------------------------

----------------------------------------

----------------------------------------

----------------------------------------

----------------------------------------

"Practice appreciation for who you are and what you
have... and allow your life to unfold in the most
amazing way."
— Millen Livis

Daily Journal

----------------------------------------

----------------------------------------

----------------------------------------

----------------------------------------

----------------------------------------

----------------------------------------

----------------------------------------

----------------------------------------

Day _____   Date _____

Today I Am Happy Because:

---------------------------------------------------

---------------------------------------------------

---------------------------------------------------

---------------------------------------------------

---------------------------------------------------

---------------------------------------------------

*"When you overlook the small blessings in your life,
chances are that no amount of blessings would ever
make you happy."*
*— Edmond Mbiaka*

## Daily Journal

---------------------------------------------------

---------------------------------------------------

---------------------------------------------------

---------------------------------------------------

---------------------------------------------------

---------------------------------------------------

---------------------------------------------------

Day _____ Date _____

Today I Am Happy Because:

--------------------------------------------------

--------------------------------------------------

--------------------------------------------------

--------------------------------------------------

--------------------------------------------------

--------------------------------------------------

*"Amidst all the bacchanal and confusion in your life, find something to be grateful for, even if it is the air that you breathe and trust me, this will transform you in some small way. Gratitude is really the great multiplier."* — Akosua Dardaine Edwards

## Daily Journal

--------------------------------------------------

--------------------------------------------------

--------------------------------------------------

--------------------------------------------------

--------------------------------------------------

--------------------------------------------------

--------------------------------------------------

--------------------------------------------------

Day _____ Date _____

Today I Am Happy Because:

_____

_____

_____

_____

_____

_____

"Always remember people who have helped you along
the way, and don't forget to lift someone up."
— Roy Bennett

Daily Journal

_____

_____

_____

_____

_____

_____

_____

_____

Day _____ Date _____
Today I Am Happy Because:

--------------------------------------------------

--------------------------------------------------

--------------------------------------------------

--------------------------------------------------

--------------------------------------------------

--------------------------------------------------

*"Gratitude, like faith, is a muscle. The more you use it, the stronger it grows, and the more power you have to use it on your behalf.. To be grateful is to find blessings in everything. This is the most powerful attitude to adopt, for there are blessings in everything." — Alan Cohen*

## Daily Journal

--------------------------------------------------

--------------------------------------------------

--------------------------------------------------

--------------------------------------------------

--------------------------------------------------

--------------------------------------------------

--------------------------------------------------

--------------------------------------------------

Day _____ Date _____

Today I Am Happy Because:

_____

_____

_____

_____

_____

_____

"Gratitude opens our eyes to miracles that surround
us. Life's a miracle and a gift. Take every
breath in gratitude"
— D. Denise Dianaty

## Daily Journal

_____

_____

_____

_____

_____

_____

_____

_____

Day _____ Date _____

Today I Am Happy Because:

_____

_____

_____

_____

_____

_____

*"Throughout the day, anytime you find yourself
feeling stressed or wanting to complain, stop for 10
seconds and breathe. Count your breaths
and your blessings."*
*— Jon Gordon*

## Daily Journal

_____

_____

_____

_____

_____

_____

_____

_____

Day _____ Date _____

Today I Am Happy Because:

---------------------------------------------------------

---------------------------------------------------------

---------------------------------------------------------

---------------------------------------------------------

---------------------------------------------------------

---------------------------------------------------------

*"Approach the goal you've set with a positive, grateful attitude, and your perception about the goal and the journey will feel less like work, and more like fun." — John Manning*

## Daily Journal

---------------------------------------------------------

---------------------------------------------------------

---------------------------------------------------------

---------------------------------------------------------

---------------------------------------------------------

---------------------------------------------------------

---------------------------------------------------------

---------------------------------------------------------

---------------------------------------------------------

Day _____ Date _____

Today I Am Happy Because:

_____

_____

_____

_____

_____

_____

*"Focus on your daily blessings, future opportunities and possibilities, and never allow your challenges, struggles, and obstacles to interfere with your peace of mind. You owe abundant happiness and success to your inner-self." — Edmond Mbiaka*

## Daily Journal

_____

_____

_____

_____

_____

_____

_____

_____

Day _____ Date _____

Today I Am Happy Because:

----------------------------------------------------

----------------------------------------------------

----------------------------------------------------

----------------------------------------------------

----------------------------------------------------

----------------------------------------------------

*"This morning I woke up, how blessed I am*
*Eyes to see, a voice to speak*
*Words to read and love to feel?*
*If this isn't something to be thankful for, I'm not sure*
*what is." — Nikki Rowe*

## Daily Journal

----------------------------------------------------

----------------------------------------------------

----------------------------------------------------

----------------------------------------------------

----------------------------------------------------

----------------------------------------------------

----------------------------------------------------

----------------------------------------------------

Day _____ Date _____

Today I Am Happy Because:

------------------------------------------------------

------------------------------------------------------

------------------------------------------------------

------------------------------------------------------

------------------------------------------------------

------------------------------------------------------

"... most of my prayers are expressions of sheer
gratitude for the fullness of my contentment."
— Elizabeth Gilbert

## Daily Journal

------------------------------------------------------

------------------------------------------------------

------------------------------------------------------

------------------------------------------------------

------------------------------------------------------

------------------------------------------------------

------------------------------------------------------

------------------------------------------------------

Day _____  Date _____

Today I Am Happy Because:

_____

_____

_____

_____

_____

_____

"When you arise in the morning, give thanks for the
morning light, for your life and strength. Give
thanks for your food and the joy of living, If you see
no reason for giving thanks, the fault lies with
yourself." — Tecumseh

## Daily Journal

_____

_____

_____

_____

_____

_____

_____

_____

Day _____     Date _____

Today I Am Happy Because:

_____

_____

_____

_____

_____

_____


"Gratitude is the key to manifestation, for gratitude
connects you directly to the source.
Keep your head up and heart open. And make
"Thank You" your mantra of life!
— Abhishek Kumar

*Daily Journal*

_____

_____

_____

_____

_____

_____

_____

_____

Day _____ Date _____

Today I Am Happy Because:

-------------------------------------------------

-------------------------------------------------

-------------------------------------------------

-------------------------------------------------

-------------------------------------------------

-------------------------------------------------

*"When last did u sit back and took an opportunity to lookup and thank the Heavens above for blessing you with what you have and continuing to open doors for you every time you knock "and sometimes letting you in through the window" because not all doors are as beautiful on the inside as they are on the inside" — Katlego Semusa*

## Daily Journal

-------------------------------------------------

-------------------------------------------------

-------------------------------------------------

-------------------------------------------------

-------------------------------------------------

-------------------------------------------------

-------------------------------------------------

-------------------------------------------------

Day _____ Date _____

Today I Am Happy Because:

-------------------------------------------------

-------------------------------------------------

-------------------------------------------------

-------------------------------------------------

-------------------------------------------------

-------------------------------------------------

*"The most fortunate are those who have a wonderful capacity to appreciate again and again, freshly and naively, the basic goods of life, with awe, pleasure, wonder and even ecstasy."*
*— Abraham Maslow*

## Daily Journal

-------------------------------------------------

-------------------------------------------------

-------------------------------------------------

-------------------------------------------------

-------------------------------------------------

-------------------------------------------------

-------------------------------------------------

-------------------------------------------------

Day _____  Date _____

Today I Am Happy Because:

------------------------------------------------------------
------------------------------------------------------------
------------------------------------------------------------
------------------------------------------------------------
------------------------------------------------------------
------------------------------------------------------------

"Feeling entitled is the opposite of feeling grateful.
Gratitude opens the heart, entitlement closes it."
— Paul Gibbons

Daily Journal

------------------------------------------------------------
------------------------------------------------------------
------------------------------------------------------------
------------------------------------------------------------
------------------------------------------------------------
------------------------------------------------------------
------------------------------------------------------------
------------------------------------------------------------

Day _____     Date _____

Today I Am Happy Because:

------------------------------------------------

------------------------------------------------

------------------------------------------------

------------------------------------------------

------------------------------------------------

------------------------------------------------

*"Gratitude should run through our veins, it
should reside in us, it should live in
our bones as long we live."*
*— Euginia Herlihy*

## Daily Journal

------------------------------------------------

------------------------------------------------

------------------------------------------------

------------------------------------------------

------------------------------------------------

------------------------------------------------

------------------------------------------------

------------------------------------------------

Day _____     Date _____

Today I Am Happy Because:

---------------------------------------------

---------------------------------------------

---------------------------------------------

---------------------------------------------

---------------------------------------------

---------------------------------------------

*"The more we express thanks, the more gratitude we feel. The more gratitude we feel, the more we express thanks. It's circular, and it leads to a happier life."*
*— Steve Goodier*

## Daily Journal

---------------------------------------------

---------------------------------------------

---------------------------------------------

---------------------------------------------

---------------------------------------------

---------------------------------------------

---------------------------------------------

---------------------------------------------

Day _____ Date _____

Today I Am Happy Because:

-------------------------------------------------

-------------------------------------------------

-------------------------------------------------

-------------------------------------------------

-------------------------------------------------

-------------------------------------------------

"If I do not feel a sense of joy in God's creation, if I
forget to offer the world back to God with
thankfulness, I have advanced very little upon the
Way. I have not yet learnt to be truly human. For it is
only through thanksgiving that I can become
myself." — Kallistos Ware

_Daily Journal_

-------------------------------------------------

-------------------------------------------------

-------------------------------------------------

-------------------------------------------------

-------------------------------------------------

-------------------------------------------------

-------------------------------------------------

-------------------------------------------------

Day _____    Date _____

Today I Am Happy Because:

------------------------------------------------

------------------------------------------------

------------------------------------------------

------------------------------------------------

------------------------------------------------

------------------------------------------------

*"There is no prescription for finding moments of gratitude in every day; there is simply the choice."*
— Gillian Deacon

## Daily Journal

------------------------------------------------

------------------------------------------------

------------------------------------------------

------------------------------------------------

------------------------------------------------

------------------------------------------------

------------------------------------------------

------------------------------------------------

Day _____ Date _____

Today I Am Happy Because:

_____

_____

_____

_____

_____

_____

"We all feel better when we are grateful. There is
great wisdom in understanding that no matter the
situation, there is always something for which we
can choose to be grateful."
— Andy Andrews

Daily Journal

_____

_____

_____

_____

_____

_____

_____

_____

Day _____  Date _____

Today I Am Happy Because:

----------------------------------------------------------------

----------------------------------------------------------------

----------------------------------------------------------------

----------------------------------------------------------------

----------------------------------------------------------------

----------------------------------------------------------------

*"The most beautiful moments in life are moments when you are expressing your joy, not when you are seeking it."*
*— Jaggi Vasudev*

## Daily Journal

----------------------------------------------------------------

----------------------------------------------------------------

----------------------------------------------------------------

----------------------------------------------------------------

----------------------------------------------------------------

----------------------------------------------------------------

----------------------------------------------------------------

----------------------------------------------------------------

Day _____     Date _____

Today I Am Happy Because:

-----------------------------------------------------------

-----------------------------------------------------------

-----------------------------------------------------------

-----------------------------------------------------------

-----------------------------------------------------------

-----------------------------------------------------------

"Grow in a way without losing much of our inner
childlike deep senses embracing truthful, pure,
simple relief of appreciation and gratitude."
— Angelica Hopes

## Daily Journal

-----------------------------------------------------------

-----------------------------------------------------------

-----------------------------------------------------------

-----------------------------------------------------------

-----------------------------------------------------------

-----------------------------------------------------------

-----------------------------------------------------------

-----------------------------------------------------------

Day _____ Date _____

Today I Am Happy Because:

_____

_____

_____

_____

_____

_____

"Feeling grateful is good; showing appreciation to
those you feel grateful to is sublime."
— Andy Lacroix

<u>Daily Journal</u>

_____

_____

_____

_____

_____

_____

_____

_____

Day _____   Date _____

Today I Am Happy Because:

-------------------------------------------------

-------------------------------------------------

-------------------------------------------------

-------------------------------------------------

-------------------------------------------------

-------------------------------------------------

"Be grateful for life. Show gratitude to others,
whether it's verbally or energetically, it has
the same effect."
— Kasi Kaye Iliopoulos

<u>Daily Journal</u>

-------------------------------------------------

-------------------------------------------------

-------------------------------------------------

-------------------------------------------------

-------------------------------------------------

-------------------------------------------------

-------------------------------------------------

-------------------------------------------------

Day _____    Date _____

Today I Am Happy Because:

------------------------------------------------------

------------------------------------------------------

------------------------------------------------------

------------------------------------------------------

------------------------------------------------------

------------------------------------------------------

"I count myself lucky, having long ago won a lottery
paid to me in seven sunrises a week for life."
— Robert Brault

Daily Journal

------------------------------------------------------

------------------------------------------------------

------------------------------------------------------

------------------------------------------------------

------------------------------------------------------

------------------------------------------------------

------------------------------------------------------

------------------------------------------------------

Day _____     Date _____

Today I Am Happy Because:

_____

_____

_____

_____

_____

_____

1. Woke up ✓
2. Air to breath ✓
3. Food to eat ✓
4. Roof over head ✓
...yep, it's a Good day!"
— Russell Kyle

## Daily Journal

_____

_____

_____

_____

_____

_____

_____

_____

Day _____  Date _____

Today I Am Happy Because:

--------------------------------------------

--------------------------------------------

--------------------------------------------

--------------------------------------------

--------------------------------------------

--------------------------------------------

"The Power of Thank You goes a very long way! Its
healing embodiment of gratitude is a key element to
living a happier life."
— Angie Karan Krezos

<u>Daily Journal</u>

--------------------------------------------

--------------------------------------------

--------------------------------------------

--------------------------------------------

--------------------------------------------

--------------------------------------------

--------------------------------------------

Day _____  Date _____

Today I Am Happy Because:

_____

_____

_____

_____

_____

_____

*"Nothing is so fundamental to the spiritual life as learning to give thanks."*
*— Gordon T. Smith*

## Daily Journal

_____

_____

_____

_____

_____

_____

_____

_____

Day _____ Date _____

Today I Am Happy Because:

------------------------------------------------

------------------------------------------------

------------------------------------------------

------------------------------------------------

------------------------------------------------

------------------------------------------------

*"When you open to your heart, your entire world changes--it opens up around you. You see yourself as part of a friendly universe, one that is full of possibility, one that is generating and regenerating a positive energy." — Baptist de Pape*

## Daily Journal

------------------------------------------------

------------------------------------------------

------------------------------------------------

------------------------------------------------

------------------------------------------------

------------------------------------------------

------------------------------------------------

------------------------------------------------

Day _____    Date _____

Today I Am Happy Because:

---------------------------------------------

---------------------------------------------

---------------------------------------------

---------------------------------------------

---------------------------------------------

---------------------------------------------

*"You must love yourself first to the soul*
*of your aura..."*
*— Jennifer Pierre*

## Daily Journal

---------------------------------------------

---------------------------------------------

---------------------------------------------

---------------------------------------------

---------------------------------------------

---------------------------------------------

---------------------------------------------

---------------------------------------------

Day _____ Date _____

Today I Am Happy Because:

---------------------------------------------------

---------------------------------------------------

---------------------------------------------------

---------------------------------------------------

---------------------------------------------------

---------------------------------------------------

*"The height of our success is marked at the depth of
our gratitude."*
*— Terry Crouson*

## Daily Journal

---------------------------------------------------

---------------------------------------------------

---------------------------------------------------

---------------------------------------------------

---------------------------------------------------

---------------------------------------------------

---------------------------------------------------

---------------------------------------------------

Day _____  Date _____

Today I Am Happy Because:

----------------------------------------

----------------------------------------

----------------------------------------

----------------------------------------

----------------------------------------

----------------------------------------

*"If the heights of our joy are measured by the depths
of our gratitude, and gratitude is but a way of
seeing, a spiritual perspective of smallness might offer
a vital way of seeing especially conducive to
gratitude" — Ann Voskamp*

<u>Daily Journal</u>

----------------------------------------

----------------------------------------

----------------------------------------

----------------------------------------

----------------------------------------

----------------------------------------

----------------------------------------

----------------------------------------

Day _____ Date _____

Today I Am Happy Because:

------------------------------------------------

------------------------------------------------

------------------------------------------------

------------------------------------------------

------------------------------------------------

------------------------------------------------

*"When your heart aligns with the truth of its energy,
GRATITUDE sings your name, LOVE flows freely, and
every bit of your being is awakened, breathing and
moving in perfect HARMONY."*
*— Angie Karan Krezos*

Daily Journal

------------------------------------------------

------------------------------------------------

------------------------------------------------

------------------------------------------------

------------------------------------------------

------------------------------------------------

------------------------------------------------

------------------------------------------------

Day _____     Date _____

Today I Am Happy Because:

------------------------------------------------

------------------------------------------------

------------------------------------------------

------------------------------------------------

------------------------------------------------

------------------------------------------------

*"Just as thoughts, send out vibrations to which there is a creative and attractive power, gratitude stimulates the field of etheric energy that surrounds you on a subtle level to bring into your life more of what brings you joy."— Genevieve Gerard*

## Daily Journal

------------------------------------------------

------------------------------------------------

------------------------------------------------

------------------------------------------------

------------------------------------------------

------------------------------------------------

------------------------------------------------

------------------------------------------------

Day _____ Date _____

Today I Am Happy Because:

------------------------------------------------

------------------------------------------------

------------------------------------------------

------------------------------------------------

------------------------------------------------

------------------------------------------------

"Never let them try out this gratitude, for they would
immediately discover that it supplies the first and
most important component to happiness:
Contentment."
— Geoffrey Wood


Daily Journal

------------------------------------------------

------------------------------------------------

------------------------------------------------

------------------------------------------------

------------------------------------------------

------------------------------------------------

------------------------------------------------

------------------------------------------------

Day _____    Date _____

Today I Am Happy Because:

_____

_____

_____

_____

_____

_____

*"The good news is that being in gratitude does not
require time and money. All it requires is an
attitude of being grateful."*
*— Vishwas Chavan*

## Daily Journal

_____

_____

_____

_____

_____

_____

_____

_____

Day _____    Date _____

Today I Am Happy Because:

------------------------------------------------

------------------------------------------------

------------------------------------------------

------------------------------------------------

------------------------------------------------

------------------------------------------------

"Love is such a deep gratitude. When you are truly in
love with life, every breath you take is gratitude."
— Bryant McGill

Daily Journal

------------------------------------------------

------------------------------------------------

------------------------------------------------

------------------------------------------------

------------------------------------------------

------------------------------------------------

------------------------------------------------

------------------------------------------------

Day _____  Date _____

Today I Am Happy Because:

------------------------------------------------------
------------------------------------------------------
------------------------------------------------------
------------------------------------------------------
------------------------------------------------------
------------------------------------------------------

*"Being able to appreciate who we are and what we have in the now is an easy way to journey through this life."*
— Raphael Zernoff

## Daily Journal

------------------------------------------------------
------------------------------------------------------
------------------------------------------------------
------------------------------------------------------
------------------------------------------------------
------------------------------------------------------
------------------------------------------------------
------------------------------------------------------

Day _____  Date _____

Today I Am Happy Because:

------------------------------------------------

------------------------------------------------

------------------------------------------------

------------------------------------------------

------------------------------------------------

------------------------------------------------

"As we express our gratitude, we must never forget
that the highest appreciation is not to utter words,
but to live by them."
— John F. Kennedy

<u>Daily Journal</u>

------------------------------------------------

------------------------------------------------

------------------------------------------------

------------------------------------------------

------------------------------------------------

------------------------------------------------

------------------------------------------------

------------------------------------------------

Day _____    Date _____

Today I Am Happy Because:

----------------------------------------------

----------------------------------------------

----------------------------------------------

----------------------------------------------

----------------------------------------------

----------------------------------------------

*"Gratitude is the heart of humility, and humility is
the path to peace, love, and understanding."*
*— Justin Young*

## Daily Journal

----------------------------------------------

----------------------------------------------

----------------------------------------------

----------------------------------------------

----------------------------------------------

----------------------------------------------

----------------------------------------------

----------------------------------------------

Day _____ Date _____

Today I Am Happy Because:

------------------------------------------------------

------------------------------------------------------

------------------------------------------------------

------------------------------------------------------

------------------------------------------------------

------------------------------------------------------

*"How would your life be different if you celebrated the things in your life that you do have instead of lamenting things that you don't? Let today be the day you embrace gratitude and appreciation and let go of entitlement and expectation."*
— Steve Maraboli

## Daily Journal

------------------------------------------------------

------------------------------------------------------

------------------------------------------------------

------------------------------------------------------

------------------------------------------------------

------------------------------------------------------

------------------------------------------------------

------------------------------------------------------

Day _____     Date _____

Today I Am Happy Because:

_____

_____

_____

_____

_____

_____

*"With all respect to your religion or world-view —*
*thank God, thank the universe, thank evolutionary*
*processes — the keyword is "thank" — just have some*
*gratitude and be thankful."*
*— Bryant McGill*

## Daily Journal

_____

_____

_____

_____

_____

_____

_____

Day _____  Date _____

Today I Am Happy Because:

----------------------------------------------

----------------------------------------------

----------------------------------------------

----------------------------------------------

----------------------------------------------

----------------------------------------------

"Embrace the change you desperately need. Tear
down your walls and show gratitude for little
things." — J Loren Norris

Daily Journal

----------------------------------------------

----------------------------------------------

----------------------------------------------

----------------------------------------------

----------------------------------------------

----------------------------------------------

----------------------------------------------

----------------------------------------------

Day _____ Date _____

Today I Am Happy Because:

_____

_____

_____

_____

_____

_____

*"Gratitude is an excellent attitude which can lift you
to a greater altitude if you put it on as a vesture."*
— S. E. Entsua-Mensah

## Daily Journal

_____

_____

_____

_____

_____

_____

_____

_____

Day _____ Date _____

Today I Am Happy Because:

------------------------------------------------

------------------------------------------------

------------------------------------------------

------------------------------------------------

------------------------------------------------

------------------------------------------------

*"The moment that you give gratitude is the moment that you find happiness. The moment that you lose gratitude your happiness will vanish and slip through your fingers" — Rasheed Ogunlaru*

## Daily Journal

------------------------------------------------

------------------------------------------------

------------------------------------------------

------------------------------------------------

------------------------------------------------

------------------------------------------------

------------------------------------------------

------------------------------------------------

Day _____ Date _____

Today I Am Happy Because:

------------------------------------------------

------------------------------------------------

------------------------------------------------

------------------------------------------------

------------------------------------------------

------------------------------------------------

"Gratitude is not just a word; it is a way of life."
— Rob Martin

## Daily Journal

------------------------------------------------

------------------------------------------------

------------------------------------------------

------------------------------------------------

------------------------------------------------

------------------------------------------------

------------------------------------------------

------------------------------------------------

Day _____  Date _____

Today I Am Happy Because:

------------------------------------------------

------------------------------------------------

------------------------------------------------

------------------------------------------------

------------------------------------------------

------------------------------------------------

"I live by three simple words: compassion, love and
gratitude. We need to act on these three words daily.
Doing so will irrevocably change your world."
— Julian Pencilliah

<u>Daily Journal</u>

------------------------------------------------

------------------------------------------------

------------------------------------------------

------------------------------------------------

------------------------------------------------

------------------------------------------------

------------------------------------------------

------------------------------------------------

Day _____  Date _____

Today I Am Happy Because:

------------------------------------------------

------------------------------------------------

------------------------------------------------

------------------------------------------------

------------------------------------------------

------------------------------------------------

*"This is a wonderful day. I've never seen*
*this one before."*
*— Maya Angelou*

## Daily Journal

------------------------------------------------

------------------------------------------------

------------------------------------------------

------------------------------------------------

------------------------------------------------

------------------------------------------------

------------------------------------------------

------------------------------------------------

Day _____ Date _____

Today I Am Happy Because:

------------------------------------------------------------

------------------------------------------------------------

------------------------------------------------------------

------------------------------------------------------------

------------------------------------------------------------

------------------------------------------------------------

*"Find magic in the little things, and the big things
you always expected will start to show up."*
*— Isa Zapata*

## Daily Journal

------------------------------------------------------------

------------------------------------------------------------

------------------------------------------------------------

------------------------------------------------------------

------------------------------------------------------------

------------------------------------------------------------

------------------------------------------------------------

------------------------------------------------------------

Day _____  Date _____

Today I Am Happy Because:

-------------------------------------------------

-------------------------------------------------

-------------------------------------------------

-------------------------------------------------

-------------------------------------------------

-------------------------------------------------

"If we all counted our blessings and then shared
them with our neighbors, near and far,
all our lives would be richer."
— Janet Autherine

Daily Journal

-------------------------------------------------

-------------------------------------------------

-------------------------------------------------

-------------------------------------------------

-------------------------------------------------

-------------------------------------------------

-------------------------------------------------

-------------------------------------------------

Day _____  Date _____

Today I Am Happy Because:

_____

_____

_____

_____

_____

_____

"Amazement + Gratitude + Openness + Appreciation =
an irresistible field of energy"
— Frederick Dodson

Daily Journal

_____

_____

_____

_____

_____

_____

_____

_____

Day _____ Date _____

Today I Am Happy Because:

_____

_____

_____

_____

_____

_____

"You simply will not be the same person two months
from now after consciously giving thanks each day
for the abundance that exists in your life."
— Sarah Ban Breathnach

Daily Journal

_____

_____

_____

_____

_____

_____

_____

_____

Day _____     Date _____

Today I Am Happy Because:

_____

_____

_____

_____

_____

_____


*"Everyday gratitude sweetens what appears flavorless
and brightens all that appears dim."*
*— Amy Leigh Mercree*

## Daily Journal

_____

_____

_____

_____

_____

_____

_____

_____

Day _____   Date _____

Today I Am Happy Because:

------------------------------------------------------

------------------------------------------------------

------------------------------------------------------

------------------------------------------------------

------------------------------------------------------

------------------------------------------------------


*"Every day, tell at least one person something you like, admire, or appreciate about them."*
*— Richard Carlson*


Daily Journal

------------------------------------------------------

------------------------------------------------------

------------------------------------------------------

------------------------------------------------------

------------------------------------------------------

------------------------------------------------------

------------------------------------------------------

------------------------------------------------------

Day _____  Date _____

Today I Am Happy Because:

---------------------------------------------------

---------------------------------------------------

---------------------------------------------------

---------------------------------------------------

---------------------------------------------------

---------------------------------------------------

*"In life, as in knitting, don't leave loose ends. Take the time to thank the people who matter in your life."*
*— Reba Linker*

## Daily Journal

---------------------------------------------------

---------------------------------------------------

---------------------------------------------------

---------------------------------------------------

---------------------------------------------------

---------------------------------------------------

---------------------------------------------------

---------------------------------------------------

Day _____ Date _____

Today I Am Happy Because:

_____

_____

_____

_____

_____

_____

"Gratitude makes you a better, stronger, wiser person.
Ingratitude makes you a negative, angry, miserable
person. Which person do you choose to be?"
— Tanya Masse

Daily Journal

_____

_____

_____

_____

_____

_____

_____

_____

Day _____ Date _____

Today I Am Happy Because:

_____

_____

_____

_____

_____

_____


"What I've learned is there's a scientifically proven
phenomenon that's attached to gratitude, and that
if you consciously take note of what is good in your
life, quantifiable benefits happen."
— Deborah Norville

## Daily Journal

_____

_____

_____

_____

_____

_____

_____

_____

Day _____  Date _____

Today I Am Happy Because:

_____

_____

_____

_____

_____

_____

*"Gratitude is not something idyllic that comes when all good things line up to be counted. Gratitude is there all the time waiting to be focused on."*
*— Antonia Montoya*

## Daily Journal

_____

_____

_____

_____

_____

_____

_____

_____

Day _____ Date _____

Today I Am Happy Because:

_____

_____

_____

_____

_____

_____

*"If we do not feel grateful for what we already have, what makes us think we would be happy with more?"*
— *John A. Passaro*

## Daily Journal

_____

_____

_____

_____

_____

_____

_____

_____

Day _____ Date _____

Today I Am Happy Because:

------------------------------------------------------

------------------------------------------------------

------------------------------------------------------

------------------------------------------------------

------------------------------------------------------

------------------------------------------------------

*"Thankfulness is the beginning of gratitude.*
*Gratitude is the completion of thankfulness.*
*Thankfulness may consist merely of words.*
*Gratitude is shown in acts."*
*— Henri-Frédéric Amiel*

## Daily Journal

------------------------------------------------------

------------------------------------------------------

------------------------------------------------------

------------------------------------------------------

------------------------------------------------------

------------------------------------------------------

------------------------------------------------------

------------------------------------------------------

*Need another Happy Journal?*
**Visit www.blankbooksnjournals.com**

Printed in Great Britain
by Amazon

17043021R00063